Each friend represents a world in us, a world possibly not born until they arrive, and it is only by this meeting that a new world is born. –ANAÏS NIN

Friendship is one
mind in two bodies.
–MENCIUS

A dream you dream alone
is only a dream. A dream you
dream together is reality.
–JOHN LENNON

Friendship needs no words...
–DAG HAMMARSKJÖLD

The greatest sweetener
of human life is friendship.
–JOSEPH ADDISON

I cannot even imagine where I would be today were it not for that handful of friends who have given me a heart full of joy. Let's face it, friends make life a lot more fun. –CHARLES R. SWINDOLL

A friend is your needs answered.
–KAHLIL GIBRAN

Hold a true friend with both hands.
–NIGERIAN PROVERB